Kangaroos' Lucky Escape

Story by Rebecca Johnson

Photos by Steve Parish

The big red kangaroo
was the first to notice
the danger.

With a thump
of his feet,
he was off.

3

The grey kangaroos smelt the smoke, too.

They bustled their joeys back into their pouches and bounded away.

Parents called to their sons to stop fighting. It was time to move on.

As the wind grew stronger,
the blaze from the fire
in the distance
grew bigger and
more fierce.

They headed away from the fire, but the only way out was towards the rocks.

The rock-wallaby stood for a long time watching them come. He had seen the fire in the distance, heading in their direction.

He knew that
all the kangaroos
were exhausted
from their journey.
Many would be
too tired to climb
the steep rocks
that lay before them.

He whispered
his plans
to his mate,
then took off
towards the top
of the rocky cliffs.

When he reached the top,
he stopped and looked around.
Then he came bounding down
the rock face at full speed.

"Hey, kangaroos!" he called.
"I have found a gap
in the boulders. You can pass
through it to escape the fire."

The kangaroos followed the wallaby to safety. They had a long, cool drink. . .

. . . and they were safe at last.